GRACE REHAB Study Guide

The Power of Labeling Yourself the Way God Labels You

This Study Guide Belongs to...

BILL GIOVANNETTI
with
ADALINE COLEMAN

GRACE REHAB Study Guide

The Power of Labeling Yourself the Way God Labels You

✦ ✦ ✦
Endurant Press

GRACE REHAB STUDY GUIDE: THE POWER OF LABELING YOURSELF THE WAY GOD LABELS YOU

Printed in the United States of America

First Printing, 2015

Endurant Press (www.endurantpress.com)
Trade Paper: ISBN: 978-0983681236

About the Authors

Dr. Bill Giovannetti serves as senior pastor of Neighborhood Church in Redding, CA, and teaches at A.W. Tozer Theological Seminary. He enjoys life surrounded by snow-capped peaks and pristine forests, along with his wife, Margi, and their kids, Josie and J.D. A popular speaker and author, this is Bill's 6th book. To find out more, visit www.PastorBillG.com.

Adaline Coleman serves as Executive Pastor at Windy City Community Church in Chicago where she has been on staff for 22 years. She holds an M.A.R. from Trinity Evangelical Divinity School where she also served as Dean of Women. Her ministry passions include teaching the Word of God and helping the local church fulfill the Great Commission. She enjoys life with her husband, Rob, and loves kayaking, biking and watching football! Her children, Zac and Meg, are the pride of her days.

CONTENTS

Introduction

PART ONE: I Am in Christ...

PART TWO: In Christ, I Am...

Bonus Materials

HOW TO USE THIS STUDY GUIDE

I'm so glad you picked up this *Grace Rehab Study Guide*. This is a companion book to *Grace Rehab*, by Bill Giovannetti. This Study Guide won't make much sense unless you also have *Grace Rehab*.

Purpose

The goal of this study guide is nothing less than the total transformation of your inner labels. Who do you say that you are? What labels have latched onto your tender spirit? What self-identifying lies has the devil snuck into your deep mental programming? And, most importantly of all, who are you in the eyes of God? Who does your Father in Heaven say you are? How does he name you?

The two most important labels in your life are how you label yourself and how you label God. These labels create self-fulfilling prophecies.

As you read *Grace Rehab,* you will explore who you are in the eyes of God.

The beautiful secret, as you will see, is that God has so joined you to Christ that all that is true of Jesus, in his human nature before the Father, is now also true of you. As He is before God, so also are you. It's really mind-blowing to think of it.

Scripture says, "Now we have received, not the spirit of the world, but the Spirit who is from God, that we might know the things that have been freely given to us by God" (1 Corinthians 2:12).

That is my prayer for you, that you would come to know the wonderful riches of who you are in Christ – that you might stand strong and tall in the things freely given you by God.

Grace Rehab is divided into two parts, as is this Study Guide.

In Part One, chapters 1-6 explain your union with Christ and what that means.

In Part Two, chapters 7-23 explore your new identity in Christ, examining each new label, one by one, that God puts on you because you belong to Jesus.

In *Grace Rehab* I suggested it's okay to start in Part Two, and pick up Part One later. God still loves you and so do I.

In this Study Guide, you'll also find some Bonus Materials at the end. These include a Grace Rehab Glossary and a Bonus Chapter.

It's not enough to learn your identity in Christ as merely an academic exercise. The goal is *rehab*, a deep healing of your thoughts about yourself and your God. That's why the questions go beyond informational stuff. I'm asking you to dig deep. What are your feelings? Where is your brokenness? What are the pain points in your life? Can you fortify those vulnerabilities the devil exploits to keep you from soaring to your God-intended heights?

I want to teach you your riches in Christ; but I don't want to only teach you. I want to transform you. Actually, I want God to transform you by a miracle of grace as you peel off the old labels and apply the new.

Make it Your Own

Here are some different ideas on how you can use this Study Guide:

1. Privately, to assist in your own personal reflection and growth.

2. With your spouse, fiancé, or significant friend in your life. Work together through each chapter, and pray for one another.

3. As a family quiet time, meditation, or devotional.

4. With your small group, Bible study, or Sunday School class.

5. On a retreat: men, women, singles, couples, seniors, young adults, students. Select 4-6 chapters and dig deep. Stick labels on yourself as reminders of who you really are.

6. For a preaching/teaching series in your church or Bible class.

7. In a Celebration Recovery group, or other Recovery Group. Many of my friends struggling with hurts, habits, and hang-ups, say they have been radically transformed by the principles in this book.

8. To help anyone rise above the traumas of a difficult past. Rehabbing your labels is a critical part of moving on.

9. For use in any classroom or home-school setting, high school and up.

Some chapters have more questions than others. If at any point it feels like too much work, just stop. Back off. Don't be legalistic with yourself or with your group. So what if you just do the odd numbered questions, or the even numbered chapters? Nobody will be hurt. You can always come back, review the book, and finish a year or two from now. Sometimes absorbing

God's truth is like watering a lawn: too much, too fast, and it just runs down the gutter. You need to allow time for it to soak in.

It's all about showing yourself the same grace God has already shown you.

I pray that God will use these exercises to peel off a lifetime of messed up labels. I pray deep healing from the wounds of your life's bullies, mean girls, abusers, and users. I pray the Spirit of God will use the Sword of the Word to slice and dice every lie the devil has plastered over you. And I pray that some day very soon, you will stand radiant, self-confident, and strong, robed in the garments of Christ's own goodness, and lending your strength to helping people find and follow God.

Bill Giovannetti
2015

I would be honored to connect with you:

Facebook.com/PastorBillG
Twitter.com/BillGiovannetti
Instagram.com/BillGiovannetti
www.PastorBillG.com

PART ONE
I Am In Christ...

CHAPTER 1

Labels

1. In what ways do you connect with Susan, the high school student, or with David, the shepherd boy? How might you even be like the bullies who tormented them? List 2-4 reactions you felt as you read their stories.

2. How have you been slimed? What are the top 2-4 negative labels you heard about yourself as you grew up? What are the top 2-4 positive labels you remember hearing as you grew up? How did they affect you? Do they still affect you?

> "You've been slimed. Odds are strong you've absorbed your sense of who you are from your family and the culture around you. Odds are also strong those sources don't have the slightest clue of who you are in the eyes of God."

3. You just got into a car accident that was clearly your fault. What are you saying to yourself, about yourself? About the other driver?

4. What do you think of the idea that "grace heals your identity first" (p. 17)? How important do you think this is and why?

5. What is the promise given to all the so-called losers, dorks, misfits, or ugly ducklings once they are in Christ (see 2 Corinthians 5:17)? Is this true for you? Can it make a difference in your day-to-day experience? Take a moment to daydream about what a "new you" might be like. Make some notes.

[AUTHORS' NOTE: Rather than simply printing out all the Scriptures for you, we felt it valuable that you actually open/launch a Bible and see the verses in context for yourself. It will help speed up your grace rehab. This may seem awkward at first, but soon you'll love it! Printed Bibles have a Contents page in front if you need help finding verses.]

6. Crack open your Bible (or app, or website) to look up these Scriptures. Jot down some notes about being in Christ, and renewing your mind and labels. Write brief notes your Bible too! It will help create memories for a lifetime.

1 Corinthians 1:30

Hebrews 8:10

Romans 12:2

LABELING GOD

What are 3-4 positive labels that come to mind when you think about God?

What are some negative labels that might come to mind?

Journal some thoughts, prayers, comments, or snippets from this chapter.

DISCUSSION QUESTIONS

How common do you think Susan's story is? What effects might this be having on our culture? On our students as they grow into adulthood? Discuss the idea that "grace heals your identity first." Agree or disagree? How realistic do you think it is to actually rehab a person's labels?

Definitions

1. According to chapter 2, what are the two primary labels that define your life? How do you think these labels impact most people's lives? How do they affect your life?

> "These two labels create self-fulfilling prophecies. You will live up (or down) to whatever labels you put on yourself. And God will live up (or down) – in your experience – to whatever labels you put on him. "

2. What was the last difficulty you had that impacted your identity? or that revealed your labels?

3. Imagine being invited into God's throne room. What are you feeling? How do those feelings indicate your labels for God? (Example: I feel afraid. I think God is mad at me.)

> From a burning bush, God called to Moses, just like he calls to you. "I have a great plan for you. I have something for you to live for, and something worth even dying for. I believe in you," God said.

4. If God said this to you, what would happen in your heart, mind, and soul? Would you believe it? Would you want to hear this? Write down some answers you might give God if he declared you completely fit for a mighty mission.

5. On page 23, Bill suggests a direct link between how you mis-label yourself and how you mis-label God. Take a few moments to fill out this chart, imagining how people might make that mistake.

If I mis-label myself this way...	I might mis-label God this way...
Worthless and unimportant	Neglectful

6. Let's spend some time labeling God the way the Bible does. Look up each verse and write down how God is labeled. Add a comment or two.

1 Peter 5:10

2 Corinthians 1:3

Isaiah 6:3

Psalm 68:19

> Journal some thoughts, prayers, comments, or snippets from this chapter.

DISCUSSION QUESTIONS

How might the labels we put on ourselves and God create self-fulfilling prophecies? What causes that?

How many Christians would respond to God the way Moses did when asked to do something huge for Christ and his kingdom?

Discuss the statements "We are ruined by the lies we believe" and "we are healed by the truths we seize" (p. 25).

CHAPTER 3

Union

1. What might have enabled Celeste to be so quick to state who she was in Christ (pp. 27,28).

> IF YOU ARE IN CHRIST, GOD WOULD DESCRIBE
> YOU IN THE SAME TERMS HE WOULD USE TO
> DESCRIBE JESUS.

2. When you think of the labels you've embraced for your life, which ones really seem to mesh with the truth of who you are in Christ? Which labels seem to contradict who you are in Christ?

3. What emotions come up for you as you think about being joined to Christ and sharing his status before God?

4. This chapter explains how the Bible portrays your union with Christ as being permanent, instantaneous, invisible, and non-sensory. Which of these do you tend to struggle with most? Why do you think that is? Which encourages you most?

Journal some thoughts, prayers, comments, or snippets from this chapter.

DISCUSSION QUESTIONS

Many Christians doubt the permanence of their union with Christ. What are some possible reasons for this? Is this something that's too good to be true?

Discuss the section on Facts, Faith, and Feelings (pp. 32,33).

What feelings, commitments, and thoughts come to mind for God the Father when he thinks about Jesus? What does that say about his feelings, commitments, and thoughts toward you? Why?

CHAPTER 4

Seed

1. Why do you think Bill draws a distinction between your *life* and your *lifestyle*? Why is this distinction important?

2. Review the three "overlapping circles" of your union with Christ by completing the chart below

	Union of...	Key Scriptures	Description
Legal Union	Status		
Mystical Union			
Moral Union			

3. Which part of this seems most beautiful to you? Most complicated? How familiar are you with these terms?

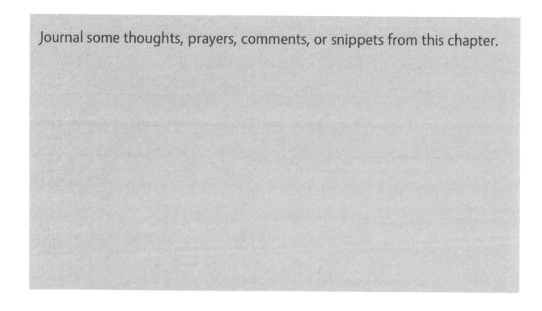
Journal some thoughts, prayers, comments, or snippets from this chapter.

DISCUSSION QUESTIONS

What is your initial reaction when you read of Lance B. Latham declaring, "You can't get any closer to Jesus Christ than you are right now" (p. 40)?

What percentage of Christians knows about their union with Christ? Do you think this is high enough?

What are the effects in a Christian's life when they don't know their labels in Christ.

CHAPTER 5

Identity

"NO PHILOSOPHER, NO HUMANITARIAN, NO RELIGION, AND NO OTHER RELIGIOUS SYSTEM HAS EVER INVENTED A SALVATION SO BEAUTIFUL AND SO DIGNIFYING OF HUMAN NATURE AS THE GOSPEL OF JESUS CHRIST."

1. Why do you think Bill included the reminder that our union with Christ does not turn us into gods (p. 45)?

2. What labels do you wear related to your level of importance in your day-to-day world? How valuable do you believe yourself to be? Which of these labels should you embrace? Which should you peel off by God's grace?

3. What emotions come up when you read, "For anybody who struggles with self-acceptance, it can be hard to realize just how warmly and easily God accepts you, just as you are, right now, today, because you belong to Christ" (p. 47)?

4. Would you agree or disagree with the assertion that, in Christ, you are the richest person you know? How do your feelings line up with that truth?

5. Do you believe that Christ's destiny is your destiny? Can you picture yourself someday radiating the same glory as Jesus? What voices inside you make you doubt it?

Journal some thoughts, prayers, comments, or snippets from this chapter.

DISCUSSION QUESTIONS

Based on your negative labels, what self-fulfilling prophecies are playing out in your life right now? Share with your group to whatever depth makes you feel safe.

How real do most Christians think their union with Christ is? How real does God want them to think it is?

What would change if most Christians in most churches began to label themselves as God labels them?

Rehab

1. Describe a time when you knew something in the blink of an eye. What do you think made that possible?

> You need to be so saturated with the truths of your identity in Christ that the devil can't stick in a crumb of self-loathing edgewise.

2. Why is *rehab* important? Why can't you just learn these truths academically, like you're studying for a test? Isn't that enough?

3. What comes to mind for you when you hear the word "wisdom?" How would you rate yourself in this category?

4. Comment about the "secret weapons" to make your Grace Rehab successful.

	Key Scripture/s	Main Idea	Where you stand right now in this
The Holy Spirit			
The Word of God			
Church			
Consistency			
All of the Above			

5. Which "secret weapons" above will be most important for you right now to make your grace rehab succeed?

If you feel overwhelmed by all the questions, please stop! Remember, this is about grace, and grace means that God will accomplish by his power what you could never accomplish. Your job is to open your heart to God and his Word. Let God, by his Spirit, take it from there.

.

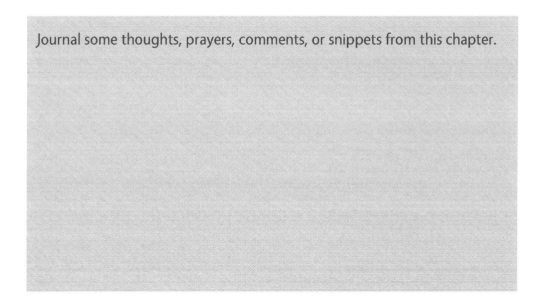

Journal some thoughts, prayers, comments, or snippets from this chapter.

DISCUSSION QUESTIONS

Discuss the idea that you "can't live like Christ unless you think like Christ" (p. 66).

What are some differences between "positive thinking" techniques and the rehab process described here?

How possible is it for God's people to truly grow triumphant and mature? How possible is it for you?

PART TWO
In Christ, I Am...

CHAPTER 7

I AM FORGIVEN

"Come now, and let us reason together," Says the LORD, "Though your sins are like scarlet, They shall be as white as snow; Though they are red like crimson, They shall be as wool. (Isaiah 1:18)

1. Do you believe your sins are truly, really, fully forgiven? On what basis would a holy God ever forgive you?

> "WE NEED A FORGIVENESS THAT MEANS SOMETHING – A FORGIVENESS SO STRONG THAT A THOUSAND SHOUTS OF DEVILISH ACCUSATION CAN'T SHAKE IT."

2. Does Christ's death on the Cross provide a salvation strong enough even for you? Imagine your next sin. Imagine God's heart at that time. What is He saying about you, or feeling toward you?

Read Psalm 103:10-12 and modify your answer if needed.

3. What does Revelation 12:10 tell you about the devil's favorite hobby?

4. On a scale of 1-10, how successful is Satan at getting you to avoid God (or avoid church, prayer, or Bible reading) because you feel guilty and ashamed?

5. How do guilt and shame impact a person's life? Relationships? Work? Education? Self-image? How do they affect your life?

> "The crucifixion towers above history as a monument to both the fierce wrath and invincible love of God."

6. In your own words, explain the link between your forgiveness and Christ's death on the Cross.

7. In the quest to feel forgiven, have you ever tried to pay for your sins yourself? What might that look like in your life, or in someone else's life? If we have to add to what Christ has done, what does that say about his cross? How does it square with John 19:30?

8. What do these Scriptures say about your forgiveness?
   Romans 8:1

   Ephesians 1:7

   John 8:1-11

Journal some thoughts, prayers, comments, or snippets from this chapter.

DISCUSSION QUESTIONS

Did Christ pay for all sins or just some?

Discuss the meaning of Hebrews 1:2 with your group in light of complete forgiveness.

How might an unforgiving spirit (bitterness, revenge, getting even) relate to a person's feelings of being unforgiven?

Pray for a deep and growing sense of God's forgiveness within your group or among family and friends.

CHAPTER 8

I AM JUSTIFIED

Therefore, having been justified by faith, we have peace with God through our Lord Jesus Christ. (Romans 5:1)

1. What kind of look do you picture on God's face when he thinks of you? Are you good enough for him? Why or why not?

2. Review the meaning of the words *righteous* and *righteousness* and jot down a brief definition here.

3. Read the verses below, and write down how Scripture describes God's righteousness. Then read Isaiah 64:6 and contrast how Scripture describes human righteousness.

	Labeling God's Righteousness
Psalm 145:17	
Jeremiah 23:6	
Psalm 48:10	

According to Isaiah 64:6, how does human righteousness stack up?

> I AM OVERWHELMED WITH JOY IN THE LORD MY GOD! FOR HE HAS DRESSED ME WITH THE CLOTHING OF SALVATION AND DRAPED ME IN A ROBE OF RIGHTEOUSNESS...
> (ISAIAH 61:10, NLT)

4. What would be different in your life if you stopped trying to prove yourself and quit trying to demonstrate your worth?

5. What is justification?

6. According to Romans 5:1 and Galatians 2:16, how does a person obtain justification? How do we *not* obtain justification?

7. What labels do you wear that condemn you? Demean you? Diminish you? Tell you you're not good enough?

8. For each label in question 7, write a new label to counteract it, based on your justification in Christ. In prayer, claim and declare that new label for yourself. Write it on a sticker and wear it around for a while!

Journal some thoughts, prayers, comments, or snippets from this chapter.

DISCUSSION QUESTIONS

Can a person ever really make themselves good enough for God? What does this say about the religions of the world?

On p. 83, Bill points out justification is a righteousness of *status*, not of *behavior*. Why might this be important?

If you consistently label yourself justified, and good enough for God (based on his righteousness alone), how might that begin to redefine your life?

CHAPTER 9

I AM RECONCILED

And you, who once were alienated and enemies in your mind by wicked works, yet now He has reconciled in the body of His flesh through death, to present you holy, and blameless, and above reproach in His sight. (Colossians 1:21, 22)

1. We all have had relationships that had hostility in them. Maybe you were never sure what mood your parent was in, or you had a sibling that might explode on you; perhaps there was a bully or critic in your life. Or could it be that you were the one at war with those around you? Take a moment to reflect on those experiences. What does hostility, alienation, or lack of peace feel like in a relationship?

> I will arise and go to my father, and will say to him, "Father, I have sinned against heaven and before you, and I am no longer worthy to be called your son. Make me like one of your hired servants." And he arose and came to his father. But when he was still a great way off, his father saw him and had compassion, and ran and fell on his neck and kissed

2. "You were formerly alienated and hostile in mind by wicked deeds" (Colossians 1:21). In what ways did your pre-salvation alienation from God rear its head? What did it look like?

3. Please take a few moments to read the parable of the Prodigal Son in Luke 15:11-32) before moving on.

4. Do you relate more to the prodigal son or to his older brother? Which one had a better relationship with God?

5. Describe one or two ways in which you have abandoned your Heavenly Father's house (his ways, his truths, his principles, his people, his laws, his worship) in order to try life on your own terms. How's that working for you?

6. Imagine God inviting you to an elegant banquet, right now, right where you are, in your present condition. Dressed in your present clothes, and smelling like your present smell. What is your reaction? How ready and worthy might you feel?

"IF YOU THINK YOU HAVE TO GROVEL TO GET A HUG FROM GOD, YOU'VE GOT THE WRONG LABEL ON HIM. AND ON YOURSELF. THE ELIXIR OF RECONCILIATION HAS NOT SEEPED INTO YOUR PSYCHE."

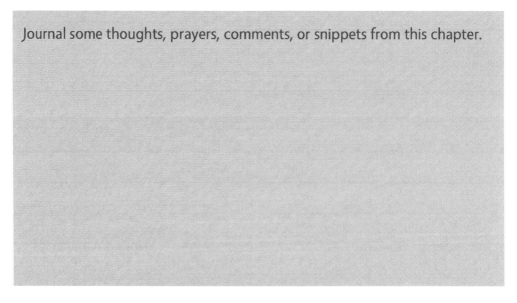

Journal some thoughts, prayers, comments, or snippets from this chapter.

DISCUSSION QUESTIONS

Discuss having been reconciled "on good days and bad days."

Discuss having been reconciled "whether you pray or don't pray."

What are some ways in which people try to massage (manipulate, artificially manage, connive) their relationship with God?

CHAPTER 10

I AM ADOPTED

For you did not receive the spirit of bondage again to fear, but you received the Spirit of adoption by whom we cry out, "Abba, Father." (Romans 8:15)

1. No one was raised by a perfect father or mother, yet the desire for that ideal relationship often sticks with us. What areas of your heart might long for *re-parenting*? When you think of God as *Father*, what comes to mind for you?

2. What are the top 2-4 emotional gaps that you feel when you think of the earthly parenting you received? This is not to judge your parents – they may have done the best they could. This is so you can deeply understand the source of some of the most painful labels you may wear.

"Your Heavenly Father easily delivers his finest blessings behind the iron curtain of earthly dysfunction."

3. What is the difference between *father* and *daddy*? What emotions come up for you when you call God both of these? How weird is it for you to call God "Dad," "Daddy," or "Abba?" Why?

4. On pages 97-98, Bill describes several ways in which God fathers his children. Which are most meaningful to you? What are some other ways you can add?

5. Scripture says, "For you did not receive the spirit of bondage again to fear, but you received the Spirit of adoption by whom we cry out, "Abba, Father" (Romans 8:15). Is there still fear in your heart with God? Why? How does the Cross of Christ answer those fears?

6. Look up these Scriptures and write some notes about being adopted by God.

Galatians 4:5-7

John 1:12

7. If the Prodigal Son never stopped being his Father's son, under what conditions (if any, hint, hint) would God ever kick you out of his eternal family?

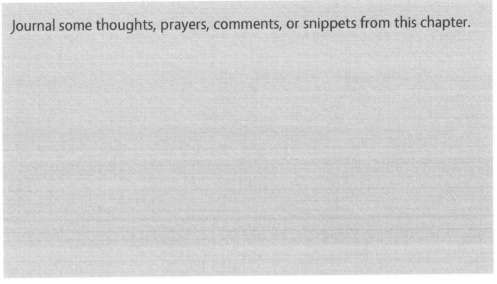

Journal some thoughts, prayers, comments, or snippets from this chapter.

DISCUSSION QUESTIONS

How might today's epidemic of fatherless homes affect our families, communities, nation, and churches?

What thoughts and feelings come to mind when you hear that God calls himself a "father to the fatherless" (Psalm 68:5)?

What might cause people to see God in the same light in which they saw their earthly father? What will it take to change that?

What are some qualities in an ideal father?

CHAPTER 11

I AM ACCEPTED

[T]o the praise of the glory of His grace, by which He has made us accepted in the Beloved. (Ephesians 1:6)

> WHEN GOD ACCEPTS A SINNER, HE IS, IN FACT, ONLY ACCEPTING CHRIST. HE LOOKS INTO THE SINNER'S EYES, AND HE SEES HIS OWN DEAR SON'S IMAGE THERE, AND HE TAKES HIM IN.
> ~CHARLES H. SPURGEON, 1800S

1. How much have feelings of rejection impacted your life? Are there specific incidents, struggles, or people involved?

2. Contemplate for a moment the feelings God the Father has for God the Son. Read Hebrews 1:5-13 with this in mind. Make some notes.

3. What comes to mind when you read, "God accepts you just as much as he accepts Jesus" (p. 101)? What labels from your past might make this hard to believe?

4. Have you ever been, "addicted to looking for love in all the wrong places" (p. 100)? What are the patterns you have developed in looking for acceptance? Name a couple. How have these patterns affected your life?

4. Rewrite Isaiah 62:4 in the first person (using I, me, and mine). Claim it as God's personal declaration to you, about you, and for you.

> Never again will you be called the Godforsaken City or the Desolate Land. Your new name will be the City of God's Delight and the Bride of God, for the LORD delights in you and will claim you as his own. (Isaiah 62:4, NLT)

Never again will God call me...

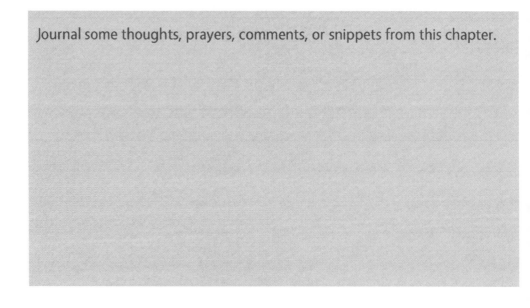
Journal some thoughts, prayers, comments, or snippets from this chapter.

DISCUSSION QUESTIONS

See how many Disney (and other) movies you can think of that play on the emotions surrounding acceptance, especially from a father or mother. Why do you think this is so common in movies?

What feelings might the Prodigal Son have experienced as he finally started his journey home?

What kinds of actions/behaviors might indicate a person is struggling with self-acceptance?

How can labeling yourself as God labels you provide a foundation for self-esteem?

CHAPTER 12

I AM REDEEMED

[K]nowing that you were not redeemed with corruptible things, like silver or gold, from your aimless conduct received by tradition from your fathers, but with the precious blood of Christ, as of a lamb without blemish and without spot. (1 Peter 1:18,19)

1. What memories or feelings came up for you as you read the story of Gomer at the beginning of this chapter? If you had been Hosea's friend, how might you have counseled him when you heard about Gomer's infidelity?

> "Think about it, because every time you make a choice that you kick yourself over a little while later, you are manifesting an area of emotional bondage. And that emotional bondage means that your soul is marching to the beat of a little dictator from your past."

2. Who's really running your life? Circle the items below that cause you stress, frustration, loss of sleep, guilt, or shame:

> *Debt, wounds, trauma, drugs, alcohol, food, kids, looks, perfectionism, religion drive for power, sex, porn, lust, need for money, fame, success, status, obsessions.*

Add some more stressers items here:

3. Write down a definition of redemption (see p. 110 for help). Be sure to link your definition to the death of Jesus on the Cross.

4. Have you ever knowingly or unknowingly accepted the label of slave? Unwilling servant? In bondage? In what ways did that label fit your pre-salvation life? In what ways does it still fit today?

5. How does the *death* of Jesus set a person free from the demeaning labels of the past? Why do you think it's important he redeemed us by payment, and not by power only (p. 110)?

> "He didn't set you free by power only – busting into prison and flinging wide the doors. No, not by power only. He set you free by payment."

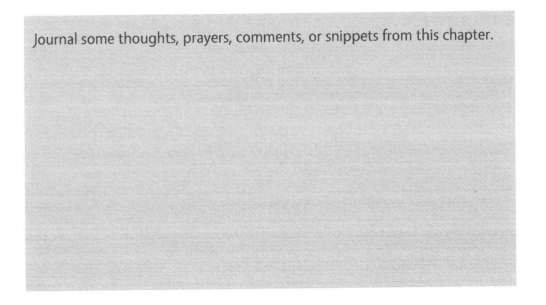
Journal some thoughts, prayers, comments, or snippets from this chapter.

DISCUSSION QUESTIONS

How does the biblical language of slavery and bondage square with today's language on addiction and obsession?

What does redemption say to a person struggling with a particular sin? Destructive habit? Hurt?

CHAPTER 13

I AM BLESSED

Blessed be the God and Father of our Lord Jesus Christ, who has blessed us with every spiritual blessing in the heavenly places in Christ. (Ephesians 1:3)

1. How did you initially react to the opening sentence of this chapter: "There is no such thing as an unblessed Christian"?

2. High, medium, or low: Before reading this chapter, to what degree have you harbored the idea that you have to *earn your blessings*? How has reading this chapter influenced your thinking and feeling?

3. Do you believe that you are blessed with every spiritual blessing (Ephesians 3:1)? Do you feel it? Name a time in your life you did feel it. Name a time you didn't feel it. What was the difference?

"GOD NEVER HAS, AND NEVER WILL, BLESS YOU BECAUSE YOU'VE MADE YOURSELF WORTHY. HE BLESSES YOU BECAUSE YOU'VE BEEN JOINED TO THE WORTHY ONE, THE LORD JESUS CHRIST, BY FAITH."

4. "You don't serve God for blessing; you serve God from blessing" (p. 119). What does this mean to you and why is it important?

Journal some thoughts, prayers, comments, or snippets from this chapter.

DISCUSSION QUESTIONS

What is the difference between being lucky and being blessed? Would you rather be lucky in life or blessed by God?

Discuss the difference between *being* blessed, which you are in Christ, and *feeling* blessed, which you might or might not experience. What do you think makes the difference?

Joe and Sally each face the exact same trial (health, financial, marital, dating, family, job issue, pick one). Joe feels blessed, but Sally doesn't; she has to earn her blessings. What might be some differences in how they deal with their trial?

CHAPTER 14

I HAVE AN ADVOCATE

My little children, these things I write to you, so that you may not sin. And if anyone sins, we have an Advocate with the Father, Jesus Christ the righteous. (1 John 2:1)

1. Have you ever been caught in the act of doing something wrong? How did you respond? Did anyone come to your defense?

2. What comes to mind for you when you hear the word *advocate*? Look it up in a dictionary if you're not sure.

3. Scripture describes Jesus as your advocate within a legal context, making him something like an ideal defense attorney, and basically making us moral criminals. Does that offend you? How do you feel about it?

> "AND NOW FOR ME HE STANDS BEFORE THE
> FATHER'S THRONE;
> HE SHOWS HIS WOUNDED HANDS AND NAMES
> ME AS HIS OWN."
> ~NORMAN CLAYTON 1903

4. To say that Christ is your Advocate is to say that God is on your side. How do you respond to this idea? On a scale of 1 (low) to 5 (high), how strongly

do you believe that God is really on your side? That he tirelessly advocates on your behalf?

5. Under what conceivable conditions can the prosecuting attorney (the devil) win the case against you by defeating your defense attorney (Jesus)? Think about Romans 8:33,34 in light of this.

6. Look up each Scripture and make some notes about Christ as your defense attorney.

Hebrews 9:24

Hebrews 7:25

1 John 2:2

"Jesus, your Advocate, stands forever as heaven's proof that all the murky boatload of evil, sin, dysfunction, and despair that you bring to the table has been washed clean, completely, in full, once for all and forever, by Calvary's love."

Journal some thoughts, prayers, comments, or snippets from this chapter.

DISCUSSION QUESTIONS

The gospel suggests that we're all moral criminals by nature. How do most people you know feel about this accusation?

In our new nature, God calls us sanctified, righteous, and good. Even so, the devil continues his ceaseless accusations (Revelation 12:10). Imagine what that looks like before God's throne, and then imagine Christ rising to your defense. Describe the scene. Act it out with your group.

CHAPTER 15

I HAVE ACCESS

Through whom also we have access by faith into this grace in which we stand, and rejoice in hope of the glory of God. (Romans 5:2)

Therefore, brethren, having boldness to enter the Holiest by the blood of Jesus, by a new and living way which He consecrated for us, through the veil, that is, His flesh, and having a High Priest over the house of God, let us draw near with a true heart in full assurance of faith, having our hearts sprinkled from an evil conscience and our bodies washed with pure water. (Hebrews 10:19-22)

1. Have you ever snuck into a place where you didn't belong? What were you thinking at the time?

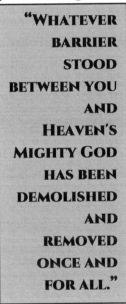

"WHATEVER BARRIER STOOD BETWEEN YOU AND HEAVEN'S MIGHTY GOD HAS BEEN DEMOLISHED AND REMOVED ONCE AND FOR ALL."

2. Think of a time you had to appear before a person of power (parent, principal, judge, boss) for some kind of evaluation. How did that feel? How would you feel about appearing before God?

3. Recall the last time you felt like an outsider – excluded from the "in group." What labels slimed you in that moment?

4. Some religious groups require preparations, go-betweens, and fearfulness when approaching God. They say it's best to have someone else approach him for you. Yet Scripture says we have access immediately, directly, and always because of Christ. Why do you think some people hesitate? What truths are they not standing on? Consider Hebrews 4:16 in this regard.

Journal some thoughts, prayers, comments, or snippets from this chapter.

DISCUSSION QUESTIONS

How does the teaching that we should pray to saints or other go-betweens square with the reality of our access in Christ?

In what ways can we show compassion to those who are afraid to approach God?

What does it look like to live every day in the presence of God? How does that impact a person's life?

CHAPTER 16

I AM COMPLETE IN HIM

For in Him dwells all the fullness of the Godhead bodily; and you are complete in Him, who is the head of all principality and power. (Colossians 2:9,10)

> "You are not a puzzle box with missing pieces. You are not damaged goods. You didn't stand in the wrong line when God was passing out blessings."

1. When people ask for "more of Jesus" what do you think most are asking for? What do they think they are missing? Be specific as possible.

2. Why do people feel they need to ask for more of Christ or his Spirit?

3. What's the difference between getting more of God and God getting more of you? Do you think it's a legitimate distinction? Why or why not?

4. Examine your heart. What external factors (money, relationships, graduation, achievements, etc.) are you waiting for to feel complete? Can those things truly bring completion? Why or why not?

5. How might labeling yourself "incomplete" affect your life? Your relationships? Your motivation? Your self-esteem?

6. In what specific areas are you sensing the gap between your completeness in Christ and your belief and experience of it? Make this your prayer.

7. Look up each Scripture and comment on being fully equipped and complete in Christ.
    2 Peter 1:3

    1 Corinthians 1:30,31

Journal some thoughts, prayers, comments, or snippets from this chapter.

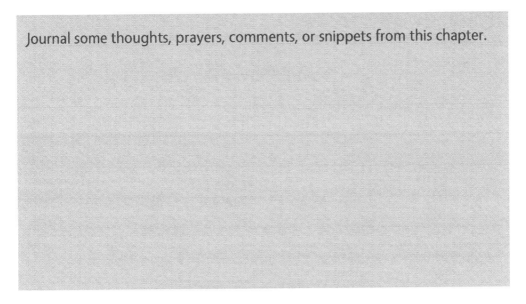

DISCUSSION QUESTIONS

Discuss some songs or hymns where Christians ask for more of something they already have. How might we demonstrate compassion of men and women who don't know their riches in Christ?

What would it do in a relationship if you expected the other person to complete you?

How might a label of "incomplete" lead to chronic procrastination?

CHAPTER 17

I HAVE POWER

I can do all things through Christ who strengthens me. (Philippians 4:13)

> ## MANY CHRISTIANS ESTIMATE DIFFICULTY IN THE LIGHT OF THEIR OWN RESOURCES, AND THUS THEY ATTEMPT VERY LITTLE AND THEY ALWAYS FAIL.
> ~HUDSON TAYLOR, 1800s

1. Think of a difficulty you are experiencing right now. How are you facing it in your own power, "estimating in light of your own resources"? Be as specific as you can be.

2. What expectations do most people have when they think of the "power of God"? What happens when we label ourselves "strong in ourselves and weak in Christ?" What changes when we label ourselves "weak in ourselves but strong in Christ"?

3. Bill identifies Power Lesson One as: *There is no official feeling of the power of God* (p. 143). Agree or disagree? If God's power were to show up in your difficult situation, what are you *hoping* it would look like?

4. Power Lesson Two says: *The power of God flows for you whenever faith flows in you* (p. 145). Using numbers, rank the items below from hardest (1) to easiest (7) for you to believe when times are tough.

___ God hears my prayers.
___ God sees my need.
___ God is with me.
___ God is for me.
___ God will never leave me or forsake me.
___ God is working all things together for good.
___ My affliction, which is momentary, is producing an eternal reward.

5. Power Lesson Three says: *Your job is faith; God's' job is outcomes* (p. 146). List some specific outcomes you would like to see in your most recent trial.

"When you show your faith, God shows his power. Even if you don't feel it. Even if you don't see it."

6. Are you willing today to release these outcomes to God? Are you willing to stand in faith with all dignity and power? Will you trust God as He works in this difficulty regardless of outcomes? Tell God this in prayer.

7. What does 1 Kings 19:9-12 teach you about the power of God?

Journal some thoughts, prayers, comments, or snippets from this chapter.

DISCUSSION QUESTIONS

Talk about the assertion that *Most Christians have more power than they realize.* Why do you think they miss God's power operating in their lives?

How can the "friendly fire" of Christians always talking about their successes, healings, miracles, and joy actually discourage the Christians around them?

Why do you think God's power works in subtle, sometimes imperceptible, ways?

I HAVE DOMINION

For if, by the trespass of the one man, death reigned through that one man, how much more will those who receive God's abundant provision of grace and of the gift of righteousness reign in life through the one man, Jesus Christ. (Romans 5:17, NIV)

1. Who's *really* running your life? What top 2-4 negative forces consume much of your time, energy, or emotion? (See p. 151 for a discussion.)

2. Many Christians struggle to accept their dominion, suspecting it conflicts with Christ's Lordship. How did this chapter strike you? Look carefully at Romans 5:17 and answer who exactly is said "to reign in life." Write it down word for word. Does that include you? (Hint: if you're saved, the answer is yes.)

> "THE DARK FORCES IN YOUR LIFE HAVE NO POWER BUT WHAT YOU GIVE THEM."

3. What would be the top three changes in your life if you took one hundred percent responsibility for your life and your world? If you refused to label yourself as a victim?

4. Can you truly say, "I captain my ship"? Can you truly say, "I captain my ship under the mighty Lordship of Christ"? What is keeping you from claiming your dominion? How well can you picture yourself as spiritual royalty?

5. How hard/easy is it for you to believe God is dedicated to giving you the desires of your heart (Psalm 37:4)?

6. Where have you strayed beyond God's fences (p. 157) in pursuing your desires? What changes do you need to make?

> "Take the scepter back, and choose the life you really want – the truest, deepest life of your dreams."

7. "God will even go with you in the wrong turns" (p. 158). How does that make you feel? How true is it?

Journal some thoughts, prayers, comments, or snippets from this chapter.

DISCUSSION QUESTIONS

What are some differences between having been victimized and clinging to the victim label?

Discuss what a Christian's dominion might look like in different areas of life: fitness, love life, finances, career, family, education, sexuality.

How do God's grace and the Christian's dominion go together? In what ways is the scepter of your life a gracious gift of God?

CHAPTER 19

I HAVE A SUPERPOWER

"For as we have many members in one body, but all the members do not have the same function, so we, being many, are one body in Christ, and individually members of one another. Having then gifts differing according to the grace that is given to us, let us use them: if prophecy, let us prophesy in proportion to our faith; or ministry, let us use it in our ministering; he who teaches, in teaching; he who exhorts, in exhortation; he who gives, with liberality; he who leads, with diligence; he who shows mercy, with cheerfulness." (Romans 12:4-8)

> **"NOBODY IS JUST LIKE YOU. YOU HAVE A SUPERPOWER – A ONE OF A KIND, GRACE-GIVEN, SUPERNATURALLY EMPOWERED MIX OF ABILITIES AND PASSIONS."**

1. How do you feel about the statement to the left? Do you believe it? Are you excited about it or does it frighten you?

2. It has been said that one of the wonders of the spiritual universe is this: "God Uses Me." If this statement is true what does that mean for your life?

3. Can you say what your spiritual gifts are? If so, list them here.

4. As you look back on your life, what *ministry* has happened because of you? How has grace motivated you to a life of service for Christ and his kingdom? Are you ready for this, or is it too soon? What's next for you to get ready?

5. Review each of the five steps to discover your spiritual gift/s. To what degree do you feel you've accomplished each one? Which one will be next for you?
[It's completely okay if you're not ready to serve God yet; it's fine if you need him to serve you more by healing and rehabbing your heart (Mark 10:45). When you're ready, come back to this chapter and open your heart to being used in beautiful ways by him.]
    1. Get involved

    2. Notice your energy

    3. Look for fruit

    4. Seek honest confirmation

    5. Don't give up

6. Do you have a church that you call home? Find a need in that church and fill it. If you don't have a good church, maybe finding one might be the next step for you. List a few possibilities and set some dates to visit!

> God insists his people act like a body, and our superpowers work synergistically to punch holes through the devil's stupid lies.

Journal some thoughts, prayers, comments, or snippets from this chapter.

DISCUSSION QUESTIONS

Some people say they love Jesus, but not the church. What do you think about that? Is it possible to love Jesus without loving his bride?

Some spiritual gifts have generated a lot of controversy (tongues, healings, miracles, etc.). How can we get beyond the controversy to focus on the mission God has given his people?

What would gift-based ministry look like within a church?

CHAPTER 20

I AM DELIVERED FROM DARKNESS

He has delivered us from the power of darkness and conveyed us into the kingdom of the Son of His love. (Colossians 1:13)

Inasmuch then as the children have partaken of flesh and blood, He Himself likewise shared in the same, that through death He might destroy him who had the power of death, that is, the devil, and release those who through fear of death were all their lifetime subject to bondage. (Hebrews 2:14, 15)

1. According to Colossians 2:15, what did Jesus do to the dark, demonic powers of the universe? What does your Union with Christ say to you about his triumph?

2. "The war is real, the devil won't quit. His primary way of getting to you is through the lies you believe" (p. 172). What are some of the lies you have believed, especially related to the labels you've plastered on yourself or on God? How is God delivering you from those lies into his glorious truth?

3. One by one, draw a big fat X through each label in the box below, indicating you will no longer accept it for yourself. As you cross each one out, thank God for your new, victorious labels in Christ. "In Christ I am not and cannot be..."

Defeated / A Loser / Worthless / Unlucky / Addicted / Ill-fated / Failure / Rejected / Stumped / Vanquished / Beaten / Down and Out / Used / Exploited / Victim / Trash / Despised / A Joke / Cursed / Possessed / Conquered

4. Superstition, bad luck, karma, fortune tellers, horoscopes, palm readers, tarot cards, the evil eye... In what ways have you been involved with these dark forces in your past? Confess those to God and rejoice in Christ's blood delivering you from them.

> AND THOUGH THIS WORLD,
>   WITH DEVILS FILLED,
> SHOULD THREATEN TO
>   UNDO US,
> WE WILL NOT FEAR, FOR GOD
>   HATH WILLED
> HIS TRUTH TO TRIUMPH
>   THROUGH US.
> THE PRINCE OF DARKNESS
>   GRIM,
> WE TREMBLE NOT FOR HIM;
> HIS RAGE WE CAN ENDURE,
> FOR LO, HIS DOOM IS SURE;
> ONE LITTLE WORD SHALL
>   FELL HIM.
>   ~MARTIN LUTHER, A.D. 1529

5. The armor of God protects us in life's great battle. Spend time meditating on Ephesians 6:13-17. Write below what each piece of armor stands for. For each peace, name one nasty old label that can be destroyed and one beautiful new label that can be applied.

Belt of...

Breastplate of...

Boots of...

Shield of...

Helmet of...

Sword of...
Which is the...

.

Journal some thoughts, prayers, comments, or snippets from this chapter.

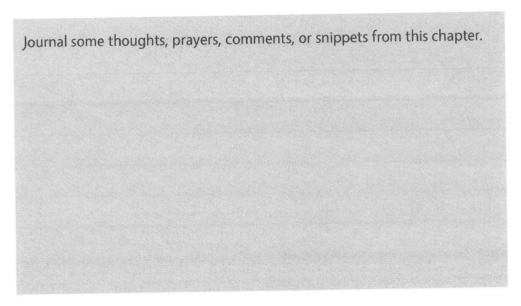

DISCUSSION QUESTIONS

What factors help make a Christian strong in faith?

Discuss some of the biggest lies our culture has accepted from the devil. Consider arts, morality, marriage, religion, success, salvation, money and other issues.

What seem to be the devil's favorite labels to slap on young people today? How can we help them counteract those labels?

CHAPTER 21

I AM AN HEIR OF GOD

[A]nd if children, then heirs – heirs of God and joint heirs with Christ... (Romans 8:17)

Therefore you are no longer a slave but a son, and if a son, then an heir of God through Christ. (Galatians 4:7)

1. Have you ever thought about each person of the Trinity loving you and being involved in your salvation? How do you feel about being equally loved by the Father, Son, and Holy Spirit?

"As he is the heir of all things, you become a joint heir with him of all things."

2. Why does Jesus inherit all the wealth of the cosmos? Is that fair, right and just? In other words, is he worthy and did he deserve it? Read Hebrews 1:2 to help with your answer.

3. Why do those who are in Christ share in that inheritance? Is that fair, right and just? In other words, did we earn it or deserve it? What would you call that (hint: it's a word in the title of this book)? Read Titus 3:7 to help with your answer.

> "GOD BLESSES EXACTLY ONE PERSON WITH AN
> ETERNAL INHERITANCE. YOU, BY FAITH, ARE JOINED
> TO THE ONE PERSON. YOU SHARE HIS INHERITANCE
> FOREVER."

4. What nasty labels have you accepted related to poverty, neediness, and insufficiency? Dig deep. What giants tower over you to make you feel inadequate or insecure? How does being an heir of God demolish them? What are some new labels you might accept?

5. List some ways believing that you are an Heir of God can change your day today and help you face tomorrow. Be as specific as possible.

6. What do the following Scriptures say about your inheritance in Christ?

1 Peter 1:4

Acts 20:32

Ephesians 1:11-14

Journal some thoughts, prayers, comments, or snippets from this chapter.

DISCUSSION QUESTIONS

How does grace, in all its forms, set biblical Christianity in a league of its own?

Why might the Christian's treasure be termed an "inheritance"? How does Hebrews 9:16,17 connect Christ's death with our inheritance?

What do material riches guarantee for a person in this life? What about the Christian's spiritual riches that money can't buy? What do they guarantee?

CHAPTER 22

I AM BEING SANCTIFIED

By that will we have been sanctified through the offering of the body of Jesus Christ once for all. Hebrews 10:10

For by one offering He has perfected forever those who are being sanctified. Hebrews 10:14

1. Review the three tenses of salvation/sanctification from pp. 184, 185. Make a few notes.

TENSE	SALVATION FROM...	COMMENTS
Past	...the _____ of sin	
Present	...the _____ of sin	
Future	...the _____ of sin	

2. How have you tried to be a "good" Christian in your own strength? How does that work for you? In what condition did it leave you? How consistent were you?

3. If God were to change 2-3 big things in your life, by his own power, to make you more like Christ, what would those things be? What would be most different in your life?

4. "True sanctification requires the supernatural power of God" (p. 187). Agree or disagree? Can you justify this idea scripturally? Can unaided human power ever intrude on God's work? (Hint: see the Additional Scriptures for this chapter.)

> "Life's ugly labels won't come off by human strength alone. You are not strong enough. But Christ is."

5. Both Hudson Taylor and F.B. Meyer describe their frustration with trying to live up to God's holy demands by their own strength. Describe a time when you have felt a similar frustration.

6. Imagine a moment of weakness or temptation, especially one that is common for you. Now, imagine exchanging your weakness or sin for Christ's power or righteousness. What thoughts, beliefs, feelings, lies, past mistakes are popping up? Begin dealing with these now. What is God's truth in regard to these things?

7. Explain the main idea of the *Exchanged* Life in your own words. See if you can work Galatians 2:20 into your explanation.

8. Of the exchanges listed on pp. 191, 192, which 2-3 mean the most to you? Why? What exchanges might you add to the list?

Journal some thoughts, prayers, comments, or snippets from this chapter.

DISCUSSION QUESTIONS

How does grace-based sanctification recognize every good work as a miracle?

Read the opening Meditation from the chapter by A.B. Simpson. What are some differences between striving up a stairway and riding up an elevator? Why would Simpson choose that analogy?

How might this *Exchanged Life* sanctification compare to what most Christians have been taught over the years?

CHAPTER 23

I AM IN CHRIST

But of Him you are in Christ Jesus, who became for us wisdom from God – and righteousness and sanctification and redemption – that, as it is written, "He who glories, let him glory in the LORD." (1 Corinthians 1:30)

1. Take a moment to review the three steps to claim and experience what it means to be *in Christ* (p. 199, ff).

	Step	Happens in the...	Description/Comment
1	Know	Mind	
2			
3			

2. Which step above is most important for you right now? Why?

3. Take time now to review the things you have learned while reading *Grace Rehab*. What stands out for you the most? What do you feel after working through this book?

4. Listen to your heart. What is your current fight? Where are the old labels holding on to you, or rather, what old labels are you holding on to? What voices of the past are still too loud? Remember that this rehab is a *replacement project*. For the new labels to stick and change us, we must be keenly aware of the lies that remain, so they can be displaced. Write out some of those lies and tell God and a trusted friend you are peeling off those labels, by God's grace, once and for all.

5. Write out at least TEN new labels for yourself that God gives you. Declare them to God in prayer. Tell them to a safe friend in conversation. Pick a few of these Top Ten from the Contents page if you wish.

HELLO. MY NAME IS _____ AND I AM...

6. Using the chart you just made, write out your own identity based on Bill's *Who Am I?* section starting on p. 206. Be as specific and vulnerable and exposed as you can be. This is your life, your rehab! Take some time with this. Rewrite Bill's words to fit your own heart's message, or start from scratch and compose your own.

My Daily Grace Rehab Prayer

THEREFORE, IF ANYONE IS IN CHRIST, HE IS A NEW
CREATION; OLD THINGS HAVE PASSED AWAY;
BEHOLD, ALL THINGS HAVE BECOME NEW.
(2 CORINTHIANS 5:17)

In Christ...

I Am Forgiven

I Am Justified

I Am Reconciled

I Am Adopted

I Am Accepted

I Am Redeemed

I Am Blessed

I Have An Advocate

I Have Access

I Am Complete In Him

I Have Power

I Have Dominion

I Have a Superpower

I Am Delivered from Darkness

I Am an Heir of God

I Am Being Sanctified

I Am In Christ

I Am An Ambassador

I CAN DO ALL THINGS THROUGH CHRIST
BECAUSE I AM ALL THINGS IN CHRIST
AND I HAVE ALL THINGS THROUGH HIM.

(KEEP A COPY WITH YOU)

BONUS MATERIALS
For the highly motivated...

A GRACE REHAB GLOSSARY

A look at some beautiful biblical concepts from the Grace Rehab perspective.

ADOPTION: In the very moment I first believed in Jesus, God made me his own child. Not only a child – but a child with all the legal rights and privileges of divine royalty. I have been brought into the forever family of God. I am the favored child of heaven. God is my Father in the most ideal sense, and I can call him Dad (Abba). My rehab really begins when I realize who I really am because of Christ. *"But when the fullness of the time had come, God sent forth His Son, born of a woman, born under the law, to redeem those who were under the law, that we might receive the adoption as sons"* (Galatians 4:4, 5).

BAPTISM: The moment I received Jesus as my Savior, God did something wonderful to me by his Spirit: he "plunged" me into Jesus Christ, so to speak. God baptized me into Christ, so that Christ is in, through, and all around me, and I am one with him. This is called the Baptism of the Holy Spirit. Every Christian was immediately baptized by the Holy Spirit into Christ at the moment of salvation. That includes me. Whether I felt anything or not, the Bible assures me it happened, so I take God at his Word. Now that I have been baptized *spiritually*, I can be baptized in *water* as an outward symbol of this inner reality. If I haven't been baptized in water yet, doing that at a good church will help kick my grace rehab into high gear. *"Therefore we were buried with Him through baptism into death, that just as Christ was raised from the dead by the glory of the Father, even so we also should walk in newness of life"* (Romans 6:4).

BLESSING: A blessing is any good gift God gives me that I don't deserve and haven't earned. My whole life, now that I'm joined to Jesus, is a God-blessed life. God gave me my blessings all at once when I was saved. Now, for the rest of my life, I get to open these amazing blessings and experience them by faith. A blessing is not a paycheck – the moment I think I have to earn it, or pay God back for it, it ceases being a blessing. I have to remember: it's a grace rehab, not a performance evaluation. For the rest of my days, I will remind myself, I don't serve God *for* blessing; I only serve God *from* blessing. *"Blessed be the God and Father of our Lord Jesus Christ, who has blessed us with every spiritual blessing in the heavenly places in Christ"* (Ephesians 1:3).

CROSS/CALVARY: Calvary is the name of the hill where Jesus died. It means Hill of the Skull. Jesus died by crucifixion – having been brutally tortured and nailed to a Cross. Sometimes, the Bible uses this word to refer to the literal wood posts where Jesus was crucified for me. Other times, the Bible uses the word Cross as a title for everything Jesus did to save me, clean me up, and bring me back to God. As I dig more deeply into the profound meaning of the wonderful Cross, I set my grace rehab on ever more powerful foundations. The Cross is the center of history, and the centerpiece of biblical Christianity. It is the key to all of Scripture, and the key to the life God meant me to live. *"But God forbid that I should boast except in the cross of our Lord Jesus Christ, by whom the world has been crucified to me, and I to the world"* (Galatians 6:14).

DOMINION: When God created Adam and Eve, he set them in authority over planet earth; he gave them dominion, which means the right to rule. By sin, our human race surrendered its dominion. By his death and resurrection, Jesus won it back. As a human – just like me, except he's sinless and I'm not – Jesus has won all authority and dominion, both by power and by rights. Because I'm joined to him, his dominion is my dominion. I rule and I reign in my life, not the crazy people of my past, and not the labels they have put on me. *"For if by the one man's offense death reigned through the one, much more those who receive abundance of grace and of the gift of righteousness will reign in life through the One, Jesus Christ"* (Romans 5:17).

EXCHANGED LIFE: In God's beautiful salvation plan, Jesus exchanges all his good stuff for all my bad stuff. He takes my sin; I take his righteousness. He takes my death; I take his life. Whatever blessings he provides, he provides free of charge – it's all grace, all the way. This includes the all-important blessing called *holiness*. A holy lifestyle can only be God's creation. My job is daily faith and trust in Christ, who lives within me. His job is to rehabilitate my life by exchanging his wholesome holiness for my self-destructive sinfulness. The secret is faith. Christ is in me, and as often as I trust him to, he expresses his own holy life through mine. *"I have been crucified with Christ; it is no longer I who live, but Christ lives in me; and the life which I now live in the flesh I live by faith in the Son of God, who loved me and gave Himself for me"* (Galatians 2:20).

FAITH: Faith is trusting in the word and power of another. When I put my faith in Jesus, I'm trusting in his power to accomplish what I could never do. Faith is not a good work. Faith is not worthy of reward. Faith is not my salvation.

Grace is the work, and God provides my salvation without any help from me. Faith is just my weak, imperfect *yes* to God's paid-in-full gift. Faith, in itself, is no big deal. I have faith a thousand times a day, and hardly even notice. Even little kids have faith. *Everybody* believes in something. No, the big deal is not my faith; the big deal is the one my faith is in: my precious Savior. All the good stuff is found in him. I bring nothing to the table but my need; he brings everything I could ever hope for and more. Like everything else in my life with God, my Grace Rehab flows into me by grace through faith. *"Ho! Everyone who thirsts, / Come to the waters; / And you who have no money, / Come, buy and eat. / Yes, come, buy wine and milk / Without money and without price" (Isaiah 55:1).*

GOSPEL: The gospel is the mind-blowing, good news of salvation by grace alone through faith alone in Christ alone. If I really understand the gospel, it sounds too good to be true. Its *centerpiece* is the Cross of Christ. Its *nature* is that of a gift of grace, full and free. Its *requirement* is simple faith, without works, effort, or even a hint of payment on my part. And its *result* is a total transformation of who I am and what I possess, both in this life, and in the ages to come. By this gospel of grace, I believed in Jesus as my Savior. In that instant, I was saved, born again, and placed into permanent union with Christ. Everything important about me changed, because the gospel is the power of God. The gospel is step one in my grace rehab. If you have not yet believed the gospel, work through the final section of this Study Guide. *"For I am not ashamed of the gospel of Christ, for it is the power of God to salvation for everyone who believes, for the Jew first and also for the Greek" (Romans 1:16).*

GRACE: Grace is God doing for me what I cannot do for myself. Grace is all that God is free to do for me because Jesus died on the Cross. Grace is God working, God breaking the sweat, God striving, God seeking, and God doing. Under grace, God gives and I receive. Grace defines God as infinitely generous, and me as infinitely unworthy. Grace is not leniency. It is not God being flexible or grading on the curve. No, grace is the perfect satisfaction of the condemnation and wrath of God, poured out on the bloodied Savior, and paid in full. I can never decouple the grace of God from the Cross of Christ. By that Cross, God stands ready to label me with the same labels he puts on Jesus. I never deserved such love and I never will. There is nothing like this grace in all the religions of all the history of all the world. If God is going to rehab my life and labels, it has to be by his own power and grace, because

I'm simply too messed up. *"Who has saved us and called us with a holy calling, not according to our works, but according to His own purpose and grace which was given to us in Christ Jesus before time began" (2 Timothy 1:9).*

HOLINESS: God's holiness is his goodness and total separation from all that is bad. My holiness is the life I dream for but never could achieve without God's power and grace. It is wholesomeness, purity, whole-ness, and joy. Holiness is happiness without corruption, love without dysfunction, and peace without interruption. Holiness is Jesus – Christ himself, living in me by the Mystical Union. When God looks at me, he sees me as holy as Jesus is. I consider this a miracle. As Christ expresses his own heart through me, I become increasingly holy in my thoughts and behaviors. I become like him, not only in my God-given *life*, but in my everyday *lifestyle* too. *"To grant us that we, Being delivered from the hand of our enemies, Might serve Him without fear, In holiness and righteousness before Him all the days of our life" (Luke 1:74, 75).*

IDENTITY: My identity is who I am. My behaviors may not always match my identity – but that doesn't change anything. My identity labels my nature, my essence, the core of *me*. Before I knew Jesus, my identity was broken down by sin. The labels of

defeat and despair defined me. My heart was enslaved to dark forces of this fallen world. But now that I know Jesus, he defines me. I share his identity – and God labels me just as he labels Jesus. This is the heart of the gospel, and it is the secret of grace rehabbing this broken heart of mine. *"And such were some of you. But you were washed, but you were sanctified, but you were justified in the name of the Lord Jesus and by the Spirit of our God" (1 Corinthians 6:11).*

IN CHRIST The Bible uses these two little words to describe my union with Christ. It's perfect, because I'm "in" him, like a fish is in water. He surrounds me and fills me with his presence. His identity is mine, his possessions are mine, his labels are mine, his destiny is mine. The more I see myself the way God sees me – in Christ – the more my heart is healed. *"But now in Christ Jesus you who once were far off have been brought near by the blood of Christ" (Ephesians 2:13).*

JUSTIFICATION: One of the most beautiful, and least understood, wonders of my salvation, justification is God's way of making me worthy of all the goodness heaven can give. If righteousness is goodness that is good enough for God, I can never call myself righteous based upon my life alone. Only Jesus can claim that title. Only he is righteous. This is sad news for me, because only the righteous can see the kingdom of heaven (Matthew 5:20). In a move the devil never saw coming, God took righteousness from Christ's own accounts, and credited it to my accounts in heaven. He then examined me through and through and declared me righteous – good enough for God – once and for all, not because of anything good I had done, but all because of the "gift of righteousness" given me by Christ (Romans 5:17). This all happened instantaneously, the moment I first believed. I am robed in his righteousness. When God looks at me, he sees nothing but the shimmering goodness of Christ shining back at him. I may not be righteous in my words, thoughts, and actions, but by justification, God has declared me righteous in my standing before him forever. Along with forgiveness, justification is the ground floor of my heart's rehab. *"And be found in Him, not having my own righteousness, which is from the law, but that which is through faith in Christ, the righteousness which is from God by faith. (Philippians 3:9).*

LEGALISM: Legalism is the biggest string of snot ever sneezed by the devil across the face of God's people. Legalism happens any time I try to prove my own worthiness to God, apart from Christ. It thrives in the moist cellars of shame and guilt. It beats me down with duty and obligation. It darkens the sun of God's grace with religiosity and performance. It is the heartbeat of every religion of the world, and Jesus hates it. Legalism is the opposite of grace, and any time my Christianity feels like a burden too heavy to bear, I have to remember this thing called amazing grace. It isn't me, it's Christ living in me. A crucial part of my grace rehab is being delivered from the insane drive to prove myself to God. In Christ, there's nothing left to prove. *"I do not set aside the grace of God; for if righteousness comes through the law, then Christ died in vain."* *(Galatians 2:21).*

LIFE/LIFESTYLE: These are terms to help me understand the difference between who I am and what I do. In my life (position, standing, essence, nature, being) I am a child of God. In my lifestyle (behavior, practice, state, what I do), I sometimes act like a jerk. My life in Christ is beautiful and good. My lifestyle is another story. The goal of my grace rehab is to increasingly make my lifestyle live up to my life in Christ. This will be a functional life of love, hope, peace, joy, and service for Christ and his kingdom. It will also be a miracle – one that God has promised to perform if I walk by faith. Other word pairs some Bible teachers may use are a) Standing and State, and, b) Position and Practice. *"I, therefore, the prisoner of the Lord, beseech you to walk* *worthy of the calling with which you were called" (Ephesians 4:1).*

MEDIATOR: A mediator is anyone who stands between two parties to bring them together. Jesus is the perfect mediator between me and God. He's the only mediator. Because of Jesus, I can go to God directly any time in prayer. Because he is God, Jesus can hold God's hand, and because he is human, he can hold mine. I can tell I'm growing in grace, and my rehab is progressing, when I lose the feeling I have to somehow soften up God before I approach him in prayer. I need no saints, no angels, and no go-betweens to stand between me and God. Jesus is enough, and more than enough. Even on my worst days, my Mediator never fails to connect me to my God. *"For there is one God and one Mediator between God and men, the Man Christ Jesus" (1 Timothy 2:5).*

PROPITIATION (pro-pish-ee-AY-shun): No matter how many times I let myself down, I know God will not be disappointed in me. He may not like my *behaviors*, but he always likes *me*. There might not be even one person on earth who is fully satisfied with me. But God is. He not only loves me, he even likes me too. Whatever guilt or shame stood between me and God, Jesus took care of. Whatever laws I had broken, Jesus paid the price for them. Whatever debt I owed to Satan, death, sin, and hell, Jesus satisfied in full. Propitiation

means that God is satisfied with me once for all and forever – even on days I'm not satisfied with myself. This is not because he is nice, but because he is just, and Jesus satisfied every demand divine justice might put on me. My rehab depends on me living before God with nothing left to prove, always because of Christ and his cross. *"In this is love, not that we loved God, but that He loved us and sent His Son to be the propitiation for our sins" (1 John 4:10).*

RECONCILIATION: The war is over, the hostilities ceased, the need to run and hide has vanished away. Whatever barrier stood between me and God, Jesus demolished once for all. He shattered it to bits and threw the bits into a dumpster. To reconcile means to create peace between warring parties, and I was at war with God. I wanted my own way more than I wanted his. But when God saved me, Jesus ended the war. He reconciled me to God, and I can approach him without fear. Knowing that my Father looks at me with tenderness in his eyes and peace in his heart can only deepen the healing of the broken places in my life. *"And you, who once were alienated and enemies in your mind by wicked works, yet now He has reconciled in the body of His flesh through death, to present you holy, and blameless, and above reproach in His sight" (Colossians 1:21, 22).*

REDEMPTION: To redeem means to buy a slave and set the slave free. That is exactly what God has done for me. I am free. I am not under the rule of any alien force: not addiction, not despair, not self-destruction, not the powers of death, the devil, or hell. I am free. I am redeemed. The price of my redemption was costly: the precious blood of Christ. God didn't just break open the prison doors; I'm not just set free by power only. God paid the warden whatever was due, and I'm set free by payment as well. Whenever I am tempted to give in to forces that will bind me, restrict me, and set back my grace rehab, I will remind myself of my perfect redemption in Christ. *"Being justified freely by His grace through the redemption that is in Christ Jesus" (Romans 3:24).*

REGENERATION: The life I had before I knew Jesus was no life at all. The Bible declared me "dead" because of my sins – morally broken, unresponsive, and out of touch with God. But when I received Jesus as my Savior, God reached down from heaven and did a miracle in my heart. He gave me a new birth – I've been born again. This is called regeneration, being born again. With this birth came a new life, and a new power, and a new set of labels, as Christ himself lives in me. Born once, die twice (physically and spiritually forever). Born twice, die once (physically only). The life of Christ within me by regeneration is strong enough to overcome any temptation I may ever feel. *"Having been born again, not of corruptible seed but incorruptible, through the word of God which lives and abides forever" (1 Peter 1:23).*

SALVATION: Salvation is the umbrella title for everything God did for me when I received his Son by faith alone apart from works. Everything happened at once, the moment I first believed. God saved me and I can never be unsaved. God joined me to Christ, and I can never be separated from him. God forgave me, and I can never be condemned. God adopted me, and I can never be orphaned in this world or the world to come. The riches of heaven are mine, because I'm saved, wonderfully saved, freely and forever, by the only Savior, Jesus. *"For 'whoever calls on the name of the LORD shall be saved'" (Romans 10:13).*

SANCTIFICATION: Sanctification is the act of God, by his own power, in making me holy. He does this in three phases. First, when I was first saved, God made me so holy that he actually labels me a *saint* (holy one, Romans 8:27). This is past tense and instantaneous. Second, as God by his grace rehabs my heart, I increasingly live, think, and choose in ways that are holy – and God by his power is sanctifying me. This is present tense an ongoing. Third, one day I will see

God face to face in heaven, and on that day, I will be as sanctified in my behavior as I have been in my status. Sin will not even be a speck of lint on my heavenly lapel, and I will be as holy in my behavior as the Lord Jesus Christ. All of this is God's power and grace in operation. Christ is not only my Sanctifier, he is my sanctification. My task is to keep on believing that what God has said is true enough to act like it. *"But of Him you are in Christ Jesus, who became for us wisdom from God – and righteousness and sanctification and redemption – that, as it is written, 'He who glories, let him glory in the LORD'" (1 Corinthians 1:30, 31).*

UNION WITH CHRIST: In the very first nano-second I put my faith in Jesus to save me from my sins, God did something irreversible and undeserved: God joined me to Jesus so that I became one with him. This is the heart and soul of my salvation. It means that everything Jesus is, I am. Everything Jesus has, I have. His life counts for me. His death counts for me. His resurrection counts for me. His endless glory counts for me. Christ is mine, and I am his forever. As Jesus is in the eyes of God, so am I. Nobody else may see anything good in me, but God does. He sees me joined to Christ forever, and I am beautiful in him. Right now, my glory is hidden. One day, I will be revealed as I truly am for all the world to see. On that day, my grace rehab will be complete – joy will overwhelm my soul, and praises for my God will gush from my lips. Until that day, I live in union with Christ, and seek by grace to walk worthy of my high calling in him. *If then you were raised with Christ, seek those things which are above, where Christ is, sitting at the right hand of God. "Set your mind on things above, not on things on the earth. For you died, and your life is hidden with Christ in God. When Christ who is our life appears, then you also will appear with Him in glory" (Colossians 3:1-4).*

BONUS CHAPTER

I AM AN AMBASSADOR

Meditation

The One who calls you to go into all the world and preach the Gospel to every creature, is the One who by your consent, goes into all the world and preaches the Gospel to every creature through you! ~Major Ian Thomas, 1900s

I can't help thinking of the old woman who started out when the war commenced with a poker in her hand. When asked what she was going to do with it she said: "I can't do much with it, but I can show what side I'm on." My friends, even if you can't do much, show to which side you belong. ~D. L. Moody, 1800s

Scripture

Now then, we are ambassadors for Christ, as though God were pleading through us: we implore *you* on Christ's behalf, be reconciled to God. (2 Corinthians 5:20)

The ultimate reason I wrote *Grace Rehab,* is because my sweet Auntie Jean, now in heaven, insisted on bringing me to Sunday School from the time I was a baby. In that Sunday School, around age 7 or 8, I received Jesus as my Savior. Auntie Jean was an ambassador of Christ to me. If Auntie Jean had not brought me to Sunday School, I don't know whether or not I would have been saved.

Auntie Jean knew Jesus because her brother, my Uncle Joe, had a blast at a boys club called Pals. Back in the early 1900s, Pals was part of the burgeoning AWANA program, offering fun, Bible memory, and the gospel to boys and girls around the world. Uncle Joe received Christ at that very first Pals club in Chicago, and went home to tell his siblings. Eventually all six of them received Christ. If he had not done that, I don't know that I would have been saved.

Around that time a group of students from Moody Bible Institute moved to the farms and fields of Chicago's northwest side. They started a little church there that offered the Sunday School where Auntie Jean brought me to hear of Jesus and where I was born again. If those students had not pioneered Grace Gospel Church and its Sunday School, I don't know that I would have been saved.

If Lance B. Latham and Arthur Rorheim had not launched the Awana Youth Association, Uncle Joe would not have been saved. If he had not been saved, Auntie Jean would not have been saved. If she had not been saved, I don't know if I would have been saved.

Aren't you thankful for the unbroken chain of witnesses that brought the message of Jesus Christ to you? Aren't you glad for the people who prayed for you, taught you, answered your questions, and shared the good news of salvation with you?

Each one, in their own ways, stepped up into their roles as Ambassadors for Jesus.

The Bible says you are a *citizen* of heaven (Philippians 2:30).

Jesus said you are a *witness* unto him (Acts 1:8).

St. Paul labeled you as an *Ambassador* of Christ, and revealed that God himself pleads with people through you so they can come to Christ.

Jesus compared you to a *servant* at a Great (but tragically empty) Banquet, and commanded, "Go out into the highways and hedges, and compel them to come in, that my house may be filled" (Luke 14:23). Don't take no for an answer unless you have to.

God passionately loves lost people and wants them found. Who will do the finding? You will. You wear the exalted badge of an Ambassador of Heaven.

Wherever you go, Christ goes with you. He reaches out through you to radiate heaven's love. By your kindness, he breaks through calloused hearts. By your generosity, he melts stubborn resistance. By your noble character, he breaks down misconceptions and demolishes barriers to the gospel. By his wisdom in you, he answers arguments, and clarifies the gospel of grace – pure grace, nothing but grace, courtesy of a crucified and risen Savior.

God, by his Spirit in you, and Christ through you, is the great evangelist, wooing and winning a desperately lost world back to himself – even through you.

Say it with me, I am an Ambassador of God. I am part of that beautiful, unbroken chain of witnesses to the saving power of Jesus Christ.

Three Kinds of Ambassadors

You may shy away from the *Ambassador* label because you envision yourself getting shoved onto a stage in front of a faceless crowd, having to stand and deliver a fiery sermon like a modern day Billy Graham. Stage fright is, after all, the number one phobia in the land. If being an Ambassador for Jesus involves public speaking, forget it, you might say.

Not so fast.

Not every Ambassador of Christ is a preacher. In fact, the overwhelming majority are not. Most never even explain the facts of the gospel at all.

Yet they are still grace-filled Ambassadors of Christ.

How does that work?

In God's mighty plan, leading lost people to Christ is a team sport. Some are *inviters,* some are *displayers*, and some are *talkers.*

The World-Class Inviter

You might have heard of Peter, one of the Lord's favorite, though often clumsy, disciples. But did you know that if it had not been for another person who fetched Peter to bring him to meet Jesus, Peter might have never been saved.

That other person was Peter's brother, Andrew.

He holds the high honor of being one of the first two people the Bible lists as deciding to follow Jesus. Even so, the Bible only mentions Andrew in about a dozen verses, and in most of those, he's labeled as Peter's brother.

Andrew mastered the fine art of inviting people to Jesus. After Andrew met Christ, the first thing the Bible says he did was to get Peter and bring him to Christ. "We have found the Messiah!" he said (John 1:41). He was an Inviter.

When a standing-room-only crowd of potential Christ-followers heard their stomachs rumbling, Jesus asked Philip where they could buy enough food. Philip practically laughed in Jesus' face – "Not gonna happen," he said. Just then, a little boy on the fringes of the crowd waved his hand. He held out the ridiculous offer of some fishes and loaves. Guess which disciple brought the boy to Jesus (John 6:8). It was Andrew, the World Class Inviter.

Later, when some Greeks came to a crowded Jewish festival in Jerusalem, they asked to see Jesus. Philip wasn't sure what to do, so he asked Andrew. Andrew didn't hesitate: "Let's tell Jesus!" he said (John 12:22).

You might not have all the answers to all the tough questions. You might not know how to answer all the objections. You might not be able to find the right Bible verses, or explain the gospel in a way that makes sense. You might be pretty lousy in the way you demonstrate Christ's love day by day.

But you can invite your friends to hear somebody who can answer their questions, dismantle their objections, find the right Bible verses, explain the gospel, and tie the knot.

You can be an Ambassador by inviting. It's an honorable thing.

When a woman with a sketchy past met Jesus at a well, she ran home and told the town, "Come see a Man..." (John 4:29).

Inviters.

Invite them to church. Invite them to a Bible study. Invite them to an outreach event. Invite them to a friend who's good at this stuff. I led a friend to Christ one day, and a week later, he sat down a bunch of his friends around a table, dragged me over, and said, "Bill, tell them what you told me." Many of them received Christ. That's how your ambassadorship works.

People are hurting. They're hungry. They're lost, leading lives of "quiet desperation." They need Jesus, and you have him. You can be an Ambassador by just being an Inviter. Your job is to pray and invite. God's job is to get them there and to save.

My Auntie Jean didn't lead me to Christ.

She brought me to the people who did.

And that makes her my all-time favorite Ambassador of Jesus.

The Humble Displayer

One of the other beautiful things my little Sunday School did, besides telling me all about Jesus, was to show him to me. I didn't have much spiritual stuff going on at home. My dad almost never went to church, and my mom only came rarely when I was young (that changed as I got older).

But I had a church full of men and women who became a like a second family to me. Karl and Paul, Ben and Pete, Aunt Issy, Uncle Tom, Aunt Alice, Bud, and a cast of characters didn't just tell me about Jesus; they showed me. They showed me by talking with me, listening to me, praying for me, and chauffeuring me around when mom and dad couldn't get me to church. They answered my questions. They listened to my needs. They fed me a thousand meals. Played *Uno* and *Scrabble*. Ran youth groups and kids' clubs. Taught me the Bible. I felt wanted.

The Jesus they displayed before my eyes made me feel safe. The warmth of affection they displayed easily transferred over to God. They didn't just teach me, they showed me. They displayed the love of God in their words, choices, and actions.

You might not stand and deliver an evangelistic speech to crowds, but you can show your little corner of the world the difference Jesus makes. You can show them what grace looks like. It's God's plan this way: "For this is the will of God, that by doing good you may put to silence the ignorance of foolish men" (1 Peter 2:15).

Every time you do what is good, the world gets another glimpse of Jesus.

When you exchange your selfishness for Christ's generosity, your friends witness an ambassador of Jesus. When you exchange your bitterness for Christ's forgiving love, your little corner of the world sees Jesus walking among them. When you exchange your cutting corners or cheating, for Christ's integrity and truth, your neighbors see the grace of God in three dimensions.

Whether you preach or not, answer questions or not, or write evangelistic books or not, you can display your Grace Rehab in words of kindness, actions of courage, and choices of love. When you do that, people will know that an ambassador sent from heaven has entered the room looking an awful lot like you.

The Life-Giving Talker

At one point, Jesus held a tough conversation with his friends. It was one of those crossroads moments. Some were deserting Christ – the hassles of following him were too great. Jesus asked his main disciples if they were on their way out too. Peter said, "Lord, to whom shall we go? You have the words of eternal life" (John 6:68).

Something deep inside them resonated with the life-giving words of the gospel. Only Jesus had those words.

God has strategically placed among his people gifted evangelists. It's their superpower. These are men and women who can explain the gospel. They are gifted at leading sinners across the great divide from death to life.

My friend, the late Lois Peterson, blew away everyone else I know at this. I earned my Ambassadorship wings through her. For three decades she taught a Bible study in a cramped basement in Chicago. People squeezed in, shoulder-to-shoulder in that little basement. Atheists and addicts came. So did church people who had not yet encountered Jesus. On any given Wednesday, you'd find Lutherans sitting by Buddhists sitting by pot-smoking hippies next to businesswomen next to hookers. We all sat at long tables on hard metal folding chairs. The floor was bare cement. We drank stale coffee from Styrofoam cups. Cigarette smoke hung in the air, and some kind of spiritual electricity filled the room.

There was nothing special about her to look at. A youngish grandmother with dangling earrings and an omnipresent mug of coffee. A self-taught Bible scholar. Her Bible was stained with caffeine and tears. It held the penciled notes of years of study. Though she never spent a day in college, Lois once debated a seminary president and won.

Lois taught the Bible verse by verse. She spoke for an hour. Took questions. During that hour, she painted an indelible image of Jesus Christ, crucified and risen again, on the corridors of our imaginations. She explained how he died, why he died, and what he accomplished by it. She covered all the essentials.

And then she talked about salvation by grace through faith. She had this incredible way of yanking the rug out from underneath her listeners' religiosity, hypocrisy, legalism, and self-righteousness. Faith. Simple faith. Just believing. She offered salvation for the worst among us. Her eyes sparkled with love at tender hearts, and blazed with anger at the sanctimonious. She used Scripture masterfully, and was conversant with almost every page of that worn out Bible.

Sinners and saints sat enthralled. I was one of them (a saint at the time). It was like magic. I don't know how she did it, but Lois penetrated hearts so hardened most would have given up hope. Perhaps that's what the worst of the worst sensed: Lois never gave up on anybody.

After the teaching time was over, the conversations began. The Christians in the room conspired to get the hardest cases talking to Lois herself. The rest of us Talkers just chatted with newbies at our tables. What did you think of the Bible study? Do you have any questions? Have you ever met Jesus?

Time and time again, those informal but intentional chats led to prayers of saving faith.

Over the decades, thousands of people met Jesus through Lois Peterson's Bible class. Addicts became pastors. Hippies became missionaries. Everybody became Inviters and most became Displayers. Lois was the Life

Giving Talker – and I'm so thankful God allowed my path to cross hers. She ignited a passion inside me to seek and save the lost.

I wish I could reproduce that glorious movement, but I can't. I know because I've tried. There'll never be another Lois Peterson. But God knows.

Instead, he made a Bill Giovannetti, and there'll never be another me. And he made you, equally unique and magnificent. We are each one of a kind. A masterpiece from the hand of the Divine Artisan. And each of us, in our own way, will represent Jesus to the people in our worlds, winning to Christ people that Lois would have never been able to reach.

If you want to be a Talker of the gospel, even a little bit, you can use the last section to guide you in your life-giving conversations.

Beautiful

Grace Rehab has been all about embracing the labels God puts on you. There is nothing more beautiful than a man or woman standing tall and proud in Christ.

As a grand finale to all the incredible labels God puts on you, he now labels you Ambassador. As God sent Christ, so he sends you. Go get 'em!

I hope and pray you join that unbroken chain of ambassadors, telling the world the old, old story of Jesus and his love. I hope you represent Jesus. Everywhere. All the time. Never be ashamed to speak his name. This old world is lost. There has never been a greater hunger for spiritual things. You have what the world needs. You have Jesus.

The more you know of your riches in Christ, the more you long for everyone you know to find the treasure you found when you found Christ.

There's a weird verse in the Bible about feet: "How beautiful are the feet of those who preach the gospel of peace, / Who bring glad tidings of good things!" (Romans 10:15).

I read that and I think *feet*? Really? I think feet are gnarly. But that's just the point. If you use those feet to walk across the room, or fly across the globe, and stand as an Ambassador of Christ, even the gnarliest part of you is beautiful in God's eyes.

Beautiful.

I can't wait to meet the people that you nudged toward Jesus simply by being who God made you to be.

You are an Ambassador of Heaven. Be a good one.

Additional Scriptures

Acts 1:8; Romans 10:12-15; Mark 16:15; Matthew 28:19, 20; Psalm 96:3

Prayer

O Great King,

I am your Ambassador.

Give me eyes to see beyond the surface smiles, and a heart to sense the deep need of everyone I know. People need you, Lord. They might not admit it, but they're desperate for you. Only you can fill the empty space within them. So use me, Lord. Make me the best Ambassador I can be. Grant me a profound compassion for those who don't know you.

Lord, when I found you, I found the greatest treasure of my life. Now, make me eager to contribute my life to helping others find the treasure that I found when I found you. Give me love for lost people. Join my life with brothers and sisters who care for the lost in a church that's on a mission. Live through me so that others see Jesus when they see me.

Today, I declare myself an Ambassador of Christ. I do not live for myself, but you. I represent no one but Jesus. I live for your glory, not my own.

Jesus, your Cross is my theme.

Your salvation is my message.

Your free grace is my offering to a lost and needy world.

May I dig ever more deeply into the wonders of Calvary Love. Open my heart to deeper dimensions to the endless wonders of the Cross. May how you died, why you died, and what you accomplished in history's darkest moment be etched across the corridors of my heart and mind. May I drink so deeply at the well of salvation, that I am full and running over with a message of grace for my world.

Lord, whether I say a loving word, extend a helping hand, or do a gracious deed, may I do everything in service for you, as if for you.

Make me a missionary, a witness, an Ambassador wherever I may be.

As for me, and my household, we will serve you by helping people find and follow your Son, Jesus.

I rise today to my full stature as an Ambassador of God.

Use me, Lord, in ways great and small, even this day.

In Jesus Name I pray,

Amen.

❖

1. What comes to mind for you when you hear the word *evangelist?* Are your feelings more positive or negative? Why?

> ## YOU WEAR THE EXALTED BADGE OF AN AMBASSADOR OF HEAVEN.

2. If God were to reach down from heaven, and put a badge on your chest saying, *Ambassador of Heaven,* would you accept that label (after getting over the shock of God reaching down from heaven)?

3. Who were the people most instrumental in bring you to Christ? How did that happen? When? Where? What did these people do for you? Be as specific as you can.

4. A testimony is a brief story of your salvation. Let's write yours down here. (if you're not yet saved, this would be a perfect time to be saved – read the last bonus section for instructions). Practice saying it out loud. Here we go:

A little bit about your life before Christ. What false labels were you wearing? What feelings did you have about God, yourself? What were you like as a person?

Write down a little about your quest for Jesus.

Who were the people you listed in question 3? Tell a little about *how* they influenced you toward Christ. What specifically did they do for you?

The moment... describe that moment of salvation in vivid details. The room, colors, smells, place, temperature... paint the picture in living color. What did you say, pray, realize, discover, or feel?

Somewhere in your testimony, it's good to say that you are trusting in Jesus as your Savior and only hope. Write a statement like that in your own words. Start with, "I'm standing here today to tell you that..."

What came next? What difference has Jesus made in your life?

Use a favorite Bible verse about salvation to wrap up your testimony. Write it out.

5. Who are the Inviters in your life? the Displayers? the Talkers? Do you have a Lois in your life?

6. Write down 2-4 names of people who don't know Jesus that you can pray for. Ask God to prepare their hearts. Then display God's love to them, and invite them to a place where they can hear the story of Jesus.

> The more you know of your riches in Christ, the more you long for everyone you know to find the treasure you found when you found Christ.

HOW TO BE SAVED

Are You Saved?

Perhaps, as you've read *Grace Rehab*, you realize you've never been saved. You're a church-going person, you're a good person, you're a God-loving person, maybe, but you're not a saved person. In fact, the language about being saved or born again makes you jittery.

I used the word *saved* on purpose. The Bible uses it all the time, so it's legit. Plus, it's weird enough to catch people's attention.

If you've reached this point in *Grace Rehab*, you've read about who Christ is, and what he has done. You don't need any more teaching. Now, it's time to tie the knot.

As we do that, there are truths to be believed, a gift to be received, and a choice to be made.

Now let's hurry up and make your salvation official.

Truths To Be Believed

Without Christ, you were a moral train wreck. As good as you might be, you could never reverse the brokenness and falleness inside you. You are a sinner from a long line of sinners and, as such, find yourself alienated from God and his love. Do you believe this?

> For all have sinned and fall short of the glory of God, (Romans 3:23)

You were, in fact, so messed up, that no amount of good works could restore your relationship to God. No religion, no payment, no sacrifice, no achievement, no ritual. No one can ever live up to God's standards in their own power or fix themselves up to be acceptable to God. Do you believe this?

But God loves you and sent Jesus to reconcile you back to himself. Jesus was God's Son. Jesus died on the Cross and rose again. When he died on the Cross he died for you.

What this mean is God reached inside you long before you were ever born. He collected every sin, every failure, every evil, every dark thought, every hatred, lie, lust, and selfishness and removed that all from you. He transferred all your sins to Christ. And then he punished Christ for your sins instead of punishing you. Christ paid your penalty. He died the

> All we like sheep have gone astray; We have turned, every one, to his own way; And the LORD has laid on Him the iniquity of us all. (Isaiah 53:6)

death you deserved. This was all God's work, God's love, and God's grace. The only thing you contributed were your sins. Do you believe this?

A Gift To Be Received

> For the wages of sin is death, but the gift of God is eternal life in Christ Jesus our Lord. (Romans 6:23)
>
> Being justified as a gift by His grace through the redemption which is in Christ Jesus. (Romans 3:24, NASB)

Because of what Jesus did on the Cross, God holds out a gift to you today. It is absolutely free; that's why it's called a gift. You can't earn it and don't deserve it. But God offers you a gift anyway. Are you willing to receive it?

What is the gift? It is everything Jesus is and brings into your soul. It is the gift of eternal life. It is the gift of Christ living in you. It is the gift of forgiveness of sins. It is the gift of justification, reconciliation, redemption, and all the wonders of being in Christ. It is the gift of a new start, with a new power, and a new identity. It is the gift of heaven, sure and guaranteed. Of all the big deals in your life, there is no deal as big and beautiful as the gift of salvation. Are you willing to receive Christ and his wonderful gift?

A Choice To Be Made

Are you willing to make the choice of faith alone in Christ alone? Notice, I said *willing*. I didn't say *ready*. Most people don't feel ready. But if you're willing, that's all it takes. It means God has made you ready.

If you're willing to be saved right now, then just tell God. Here is a sample prayer you might pray to him, following an ABC pattern. This is your choice.

Here is the prayer:

> Believe on the Lord Jesus Christ, and you will be saved. (Acts 16:31)
>
> Therefore, having been justified by faith, we have peace with God through our Lord Jesus Christ, (Romans 5:1)

Dear God,

I ADMIT I need you. I have lived by my own ideas and strength, but it's not enough. I admit I have broken your laws. I admit I have sinned. I have let you down. I've even let myself down. I cannot reach you, and could never do enough to deserve salvation. I am a sinner, and I need you. I admit it God.

But I BELIEVE that Jesus is my way to you. I believe he is your Son. I believe he died on the Cross and rose again. I believe he did this for me, to cleanse my sins and make me acceptable in your sight. Only Jesus can save me. I'm not sure how it all works, but I'm telling you, God, right now, that I am believing in Jesus.

So right now I CHOOSE to receive Jesus as my Savior. I receive your gift. I choose to trust him as my Only Hope, for salvation, for heaven, for forgiveness, and for all the new labels I will find in him. I receive the gift of Christ and all he brings. I'm asking you right now, because of Jesus, God please save me, forgive me, and make me your own forever.

I pray in Jesus' name,
Amen.

If you prayed that prayer, God heard you. He has never turned anyone away. And you will belong to him forever. Tell a close friend, small group member, or pastor about what you've just done. If you don't have one, find a great group of believers to be part of.

God loves you and so do I.

I pray God's Grace Rehab will be strong in you all your days.

Now to Him who is able to keep you from stumbling, And to present you faultless Before the presence of His glory with exceeding joy, To God our Savior, Who alone is wise, Be glory and majesty, Dominion and power, Both now and forever.
Amen.
(Jude 1:24, 25)

Made in the USA
San Bernardino, CA
15 January 2019